Department for Transport

An Introduction to the Use of Portable Vehicular Signals

London: TSO

Department for Transport
Great Minster House
33 Horseferry Road
London SW1P 4DR
Web site www.gov.uk/dft

ISBN 978 0 11 552936 8

Ninth Impression 2013

 Printed in Great Britain on paper containing at least 75% recycled fibre.

Introduction

This booklet does not cover portable pedestrian crossing facilities. See Traffic Advisory Leaflet 3/11: *Signal-controlled pedestrian facilities at portable signals* for advice on the use of these facilities. The leaflet is available from the Department's website at www.gov.uk/government/publications/signal-controlled-pedestrian-facilities-at-portable-traffic-signals

You, or your supervisor, will need to discuss the placing of portable traffic signals with the traffic authority. Permission in writing will be required, and express approval to the placing of the signals at a particular site may be needed. If the permission/express approval gives positions for signal heads etc., it is important that the layout follows those instructions. Lack of permission/approval and/or incorrect layout may make the site unlawful. You, or your supervisor, should check if in doubt.

If the works are close to or are likely to affect level crossings, permanent signal-controlled junctions and controlled crossings (including Zebras), the traffic authority must be involved before you proceed. In the case of level crossings, the railway authority must also be involved at an early stage.

The system

Signal heads: the Code of Practice says that consideration should be given to providing two signal heads on each approach. However, whether one or two signal heads are used, for safe operation, the approaching driver must be able to see at least one signal on the approach and one whilst waiting at the WAIT HERE sign (see 'Setting up the equipment'). Signal heads must be either: compliant to the European Specification EN 12368, or of a type approved to TR 2206, or the TR 0102 amendment to BS 505. The information may be on the signal head, otherwise check with the supplier.

Portable signal controllers are linked to the signal heads and detectors by either:

- cables: which will need protecting where they cross the carriageway, and are vulnerable to problems from turning or accelerating/braking vehicles (see page 13), or

- radio control: care needs to be taken to ensure that other sources of radio transmission and obstructions do not interfere with the radio link.

Energy sources include: diesel or Liquefied Petroleum Gas (LPG) generator, battery or mains electrical supply through a suitable transformer.

The above factors, taking into account any environmental considerations, may influence your choice of system. You, or your supervisor, should check with the manufacturer if in any doubt about the above details.

What to do first

The portable signal controller and detector equipment must be of a type approved on behalf of the Secretary of State for Transport. Specifications are issued by the Highways Agency.

Look on the controller for a label* for the specification reference. Most equipment will be approved against MCE 0111, TR 0111, or the current TR 2502. Equipment to MCE 0111 and TR 0111 has the same initial set-up (see pages 15 and 16), whereas that to TR 2502 is different. This booklet gives advice on both initial set-up sequences. For ease of reference, the sequence of MCE 0111 and TR 0111 will be highlighted in pink and that of TR 2502 in yellow. In addition, there is one controller approved to an interim specification 027-008-024. References to 027-008-024 have been made separately.

Look on the detector housing for a label* stating which specification applies. Equipment is approved against MCE 0114 (C), TR 2147, or the current TR 2504. The detector housing may be fixed to the top of the signal head; others are fitted below the head.

If the relevant controller/detection specification information is not on a label, it may be on information in the controller housing. However, if the specification information is not available, you or your supervisor should check with the traffic authority that it is approved.

*Note: There is no longer a requirement for the label to bear a crown emblem.

Vehicle Actuation (VA) operation

Signal control should always be vehicle actuated (VA) unless agreed otherwise, in writing, by the traffic authority. You will find that modes other than VA are provided on the controller, but these should only be used to relieve short-term difficulties.

VA reduces delay to vehicles by ensuring that the green time is adjusted automatically. The relevant traffic authority may, however, instruct you to use another control mode, either for the duration of the works, or for specific times of the day.

The selection may be by rotary switch, similar to that shown below, or by menu display and keypad.

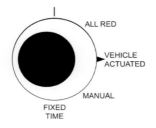

All Red – holds signals on red to all approaches.

Manual (MAN) – should be used to stop traffic if the shuttle lane has to be occupied for short periods (e.g. for unloading).

Fixed time (FT) – may be used while awaiting the arrival of the engineer if the equipment needs attention. On some controllers there is no fixed time mode.

Vehicle Actuation (VA)

On VA, if there are no approaching vehicles, the signals will revert to red in both directions. The first vehicle to arrive will register a demand for the signals to change on that approach. See 'Nudge circuit' on page 14.

Following vehicles will extend the time that the green light is shown. The duration of the green will vary between the minimum green period (7 or 12 seconds) and the maximum green period (settable on the controller). The signals will change either when the last vehicle has passed, or after the maximum time the green signal has been set for.

How does it work?

Each signal is provided with a vehicle-detector unit. These units normally use microwave technology and are often referred to as an 'MVD' (Microwave Vehicle Detector). Other technology can be used, but the unit must be approved (see page 3).

The MVD can detect most moving motor vehicles, including larger motorcycles, up to 40 metres away, but with smaller motorcycles and cycles the distance is 25 metres — provided they are travelling towards the MVD at speeds greater than 10 mph and the detector is correctly aligned (see next page). Some detectors may be able to work outside these limits.

An indicator is illuminated when a vehicle is detected and the 'detect' message is sent from the MVD to the controller.

What you need to do

Use only equipment of a type approved (a legal requirement) – see page 3.

All equipment on site can have problems, particularly from accidental and vandal damage. Maintenance contact information is therefore essential and should be readily available – for example, prominently displayed on the equipment.

Test the equipment before setting up – see pages 14 to 16.

Set up the signing and equipment correctly – see pages 11 to 16.

Use the 'VA' setting on the controller.

Align the MVDs carefully at each end of the site – see page 14. Remember, MVDs cannot see around corners, parked vehicles, plant or materials! Neither can they work properly if they are: pointing at the sky – or over a hedge, not facing oncoming traffic, or damaged by being roughly treated, for example thrown onto the back of a lorry.

Use the correct All-Red and Maximum Green settings (see pages 7 to 10).

If there is a photocell fitted, ensure it is not going to be overshadowed by, say, a tree canopy.

Adjusting the timers

Look at the selection switches, or menu display/keypad, for the All-Red and Maximum Green timers for each approach. This should make it clear whether to measure the distance between:

- the two 'WAIT HERE' signs – at sites with more than two approaches, the longest distance to the other 'WAIT HERE' signs is used for that approach – or

- the 'WAIT HERE' sign and the 'datum' point. The datum point can be half way along the shuttle working length, or a point in the centre of the junction (see page 8).

It is important to watch the vehicular flow at intervals and adjust the controller settings if necessary. As the flow changes during the day and day-to-day, it is necessary to carry out this check several times daily.

The following tables cover distances up to 300 metres between 'WAIT HERE' signs. If the longest distance is above 300 metres, ask for advice from the relevant traffic authority before proceeding. NOTE: Some authorities will need to be informed if the distance is over 200 metres. You, or your supervisor, should check if in doubt.

Datum point

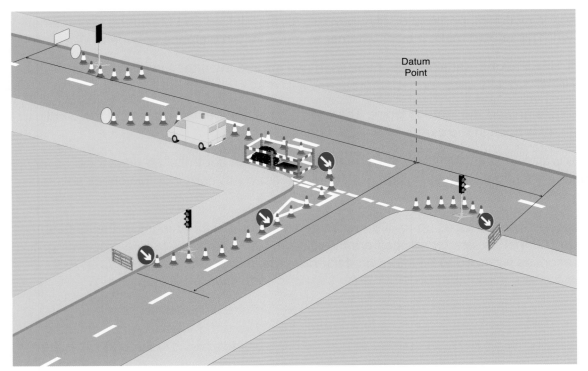

Datum
Point

Datum point (Note: The Chapter 8 triangular warning signs, guarding on the footway and possible secondary signals have been omitted for clarity.)

Adjusting the red timers

Measure the distance between 'WAIT HERE' signs, or the 'WAIT HERE' sign and datum point, (see page 7), and use the table below:

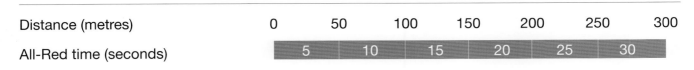

Distance (metres)	0	50	100	150	200	250	300
All-Red time (seconds)		5	10	15	20	25	30

NOTE: On some controllers the All-Red switch may be marked in metres and the equipment converts to seconds automatically.

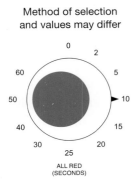

Method of selection and values may differ

ALL RED
(SECONDS)

If the site is on a steep gradient, you may need to increase the indicated All-Red value for the uphill direction incrementally until vehicles clear safely.

If there are large numbers of slow-moving vehicles that have difficulty in clearing the works before the lights have changed, increase indicated values of the relevant All-Red settings incrementally until vehicles clear safely.

Adjusting the Maximum Green settings

Measure the distance between 'WAIT HERE' signs, or the 'WAIT HERE' sign and datum point, (see page 7), and use the table below:

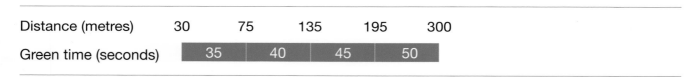

Distance (metres)	30	75	135	195	300
Green time (seconds)		35	40	45	50

NOTE: On some controllers the Maximum Green switch may be marked in metres, and the equipment converts to seconds automatically.

Method of selection
and values may differ

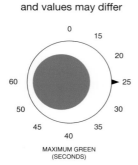

MAXIMUM GREEN
(SECONDS)

Set the Maximum Green times to the appropriate settings.

If substantial queues begin to form and vehicles take more than one green period to get through the site, then adjust the setting incrementally. For each new setting allow a few green periods to assess the difference. It is normal to increase the setting but, if this increases the queue, reduce the setting, again allowing time to assess the result.

Setting up – general signing

Check that full Chapter 8 signing is provided and checked regularly. Log any problems and remedial action taken. Make sure you are familiar with recommendations on the stability of signs and the need for standby 'STOP'/'GO' signs.

If possible, avoid placing signs and/or signals on the footway.

For additional advice on signing, including that for works on or near footways, see Chapter 8 and the Code of Practice.

Care should be taken to allow sufficient room for vehicles to pass between the end of the works and vehicles waiting at the signal. If the signal head is not within the coned-off area, protect it with traffic cones. See the Code of Practice for detail on lead-in and exit tapers.

Setting up – 'WAIT HERE' signs

Position the signals where needed. For clear visibility of the signal and reliable detector operation, there must not be any obstructions between the signals and vehicles up to 70 metres away.

'WAIT HERE'[1] signs should be placed before the signal head. If there is a side road controlled by portable signals use the '3-WAY CONTROL'[2] sign.

If there are uncontrolled side roads joining works under signal controlled shuttle working, use the two signs[3,4] in addition to the 'WAIT HERE' signs.

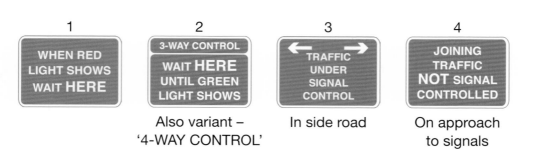

1
WHEN RED LIGHT SHOWS WAIT HERE

2
3-WAY CONTROL WAIT HERE UNTIL GREEN LIGHT SHOWS
Also variant – '4-WAY CONTROL'

3
← TRAFFIC UNDER SIGNAL CONTROL →
In side road

4
JOINING TRAFFIC NOT SIGNAL CONTROLLED
On approach to signals

Setting up – 'RAMP' signs

Many portable signals are radio controlled, but some are connected by cable. If the signals are on the near side of the road, cables may have to cross the shuttle lane. Cables crossing a road, should not be placed where vehicles are turning, or accelerating/ decelerating.

Where vehicles have to pass over the cable, use a cable crossing protector. These are designed to prevent damage to the cable and to allow vehicles, particularly those with two wheels, to cross safely.

'RAMP' and 'RAMP AHEAD' signs must be used, and it may be necessary to weight the cable crossing protector at each end to prevent lifting or twisting.

It should not be necessary for cables to cross the footway.

Setting up the MVDs

The MVDs work best if they are mounted on signals on the near side of the road.

A vehicle approaching the MVD, within the range given on page 5, should be detected. The indicator will be illuminated on the MVD (see page 5). If this does not happen, check the alignment and readjust as necessary. If the indicator still does not illuminate when the next vehicle approaches, call out the service engineer.

If the indicator stays on regardless of approaching vehicles, the MVD probably needs replacing – call the service engineer.

Specifications MCE 0114(C), TR 2147 and TR 2504 require that, if a detector has not registered a demand for 2.5 minutes, the detector generates a demand via its 'nudge circuit'. This will mean that at quiet times the signals will change at least every two and a half minutes.

Initial set-up of the equipment

	MCE 0111, TR 0111	TR 2502
1	Point signals away from the road so they cannot be seen by drivers.	Align the signals and MVDs – see pages 5, 6, 12 to 14.
2	Connect the signal heads and power supply to the controller.	Connect the signal heads and power supply to the controller.
3	Set the controller to 'MANUAL'.	Set the 'All-Red' controls – see pages 7 to 9.
4	Set the 'All-Red' controls – see pages 7 to 9.	Set the 'Maximum Green' controls – see pages 7, 8 and 10.
5	Set the 'Maximum Green' controls – see pages 7, 8 and 10.	Set the controller to Vehicle Actuated (VA).
6	Switch on signal heads and go to page 16.	Switch on signal heads. On some controllers this may be achieved by selecting VA. Go to page 16.

Controllers to 027-008-024 – consult the instructions for the equipment.

What happens next?

MCE 0111, TR 0111	TR 2502
Signals start by showing red.	The sequence will start by closing down each approach in sequence through amber, then red. On the last approach, the signals will show green.
It is recommended that, when it is safe to do so – working on one approach at a time, turn the signal heads to face oncoming vehicles. Ensure the MVDs are also aligned to face the vehicles.	
Switch to Vehicle Actuated (VA). The signals to one approach will change – red/amber, green. Other approaches will stay red until the end of the first approach green. The signals will then cycle in the normal fashion.	The signals will then cycle in the normal fashion.
	Check the timings and the operation of the MVDs.
Check the timings and the operation of the MVDs.	

Controllers to 027-008-024 – consult the instructions for the equipment.

Trouble-shooting guide

Problem	Possible cause	Remedy
Very long vehicular queues	Maximum Green setting needs adjusting	See page 10
	Faulty detector (MVD)	Call service engineer*
	Too many vehicles	Discuss with relevant traffic authority urgently
Green period always same length	Maximum Green setting needs adjusting	See page 10
	Faulty detector (MVD)	Call service engineer*
	Low vehicular density	No action required
Vehicles still in shuttle lane at start of next green	Vehicles entering shuttle lane after start of red	If frequent, report facts to the police
	All-Red too short	Increase setting
	Obstruction in carriageway	Clear obstruction

* The signals may need to be controlled by using MANUAL or FIXED TIME, depending on the severity of the problem.

Trouble-shooting guide (continued)

Problem	Possible cause	Remedy
Long gap between last vehicle clearing shuttle lane and start of next green	All-Red setting too long	Decrease setting
	Detector fault – working fixed time	Call service engineer
Signals do not remain on red in absence of vehicles	Detector fault – working fixed time	Call service engineer
	Switched to Fixed Time	Switch to VA
	'Misaligned detectors	Re-align detectors
	*'Nudge circuit' operating	No action
Signals do not change after one stream has stopped, even though vehicles are waiting	Faulty detector (MVD)	Call service engineer, work signals MANUALLY or FT until engineer arrives.

* See page 14 for nudge circuit.

Printed in the United Kingdom for TSO
J002816745 c15 11/13